Karol Wojtyla

The Pope of the Third Millennium

KAROL WOJTYLA
The Pope of
the Third Millennium

Text by Tony Pagot
Illustrations by Sergio Toppi

ST PAULS

CONTENTS

INTRODUCTION

Specially dedicated to young people everywhere, the privileged subjects of the Holy Father's love and concern

With the Great Jubilee of the Year 2000 ended, St Pauls Publishing now give us a new book dedicated to the life, character and works of the man by whose inspiration this Holy Year came about; the same man who guided it by his wise words and his own personal example: the Holy Father John Paul II. Many books have already been written on the Pope, and so it gives me even more pleasure to see that the editors have chosen a type of literature never used before in connection with a Pontiff – a comic book, aimed specifically at the younger reader. The Holy Father – as we saw again during the World Youth Day and in his encounters with children – has a particular affection for the young, which they return equally.

But the life of Pope John Paul II and the themes of the Jubilee Year have even more in common than just a special concern for young people. In this comic book the events in the Holy Father's life are narrated by a grandfather to his grandchildren. As we watch the story unfold and get to know the children and their grandparents themselves, we realise how important it is for families to be united and for their members to talk to each other. Such values have always been present in the teaching of John Paul II and continually re-emphasised in all the special days of the Jubilee. These values provide the solid foundation on which the entire story is based. Comic books are exciting and get to the point, and in this life of the Holy Father Sergio Toppi and Tony Pagot help us to get to know the present Pontiff: his spontaneity, his burning desire to meet all peoples and every person and to invite them to be not afraid to open their hearts to Christ, his forgiving of the man who shot him, his considerable contribution to peace and to the dialogue between religions, his defence of life and protection of its dignity, his countless words of faith and hope… ending with the images, the pictures, of Christmas Eve 1999 when the Great Jubilee of 2000 began.

Truly, as we read in one of the frames, 'this different Pope was the first Pope since the time of the French Revolution to live the world-wide mission of the Catholic Church, capable of changing the face of the earth'. Our earth is not only 'an old world which is dying', but a 'new one which is being born'. This life of the Pope, then, will help many young people to get to know the first Slavic Pope in history better. It will also help them to understand more profoundly the one who gave the Pope the strength to lead the Church into the year 2000: Christ, 'the secret of true freedom and profound joy of heart… the supreme friend and the teacher of every real friendship'. They will be able to confront with courage that 'radical choice of faith and life', to which John Paul II has called them, inviting them to become '"morning watchmen" (cf. Is 21:11-12) at the dawn of the new millennium' (cf. Apostolic Letter *Novo Millennio Ineunte*, 9).

My wish is that all readers of this volume, both young and old, might draw inspiration from it to live and give witness to their own faith in Jesus Christ, the living One yesterday, today and always.

+ Crescenzio Sepe
General Secretary of the Great Jubilee of the Year 2000

ABOUT THE AUTHORS

Tony Pagot

The pen-name of Antonio Pagotto. Writer and designer of comics. Born in Milan on 16 December 1921. Tony Pagot has had a long career in cartoon making. His first film, produced in cooperation with his brother in 1939, was *I fratelli Dinamite* ('The Dynamite Brothers'). After the War Pagot Studios produced mainly advertising cartoons, first for the cinema and then for television. Their most famous character was *Calimero, il pulcino nero* ('Calimero the Little Black Chick'). Since 1976 Tony Pagot has dedicated himself to the passion of his youth: comics. For the *Giornalino* he produced, among others, the long-running stories of Micromino, the tales *I ragazzi di Glocity* ('The Children of Glocity') and a shortened version of the much-loved novel *The Wind in the Willows*. Besides Pope Wojtyla he recently wrote the script for the series Cybirius.

Sergio Toppi

Designer and writer of comics. Born in Milan on 11 October 1932, he began his career first as an illustrator and then as an animator. In 1966 he entered the world of comics on the pages of the *Corriere dei piccoli*. He worked next for the *Messagero dei ragazzi*, *Linus,* and *Corto Maltese* (Short Man from Malta). He began working with the *Giornalino* in 1976 with his comic strip *L'amore della vita* ('The Love of Life') which was taken from a story by Jack London. Many stories followed, both written and drawn by Toppi himself, including *Finché vivrai* ('So that You Might Live'), *Smeraldi per il faraone* ('Emeralds for the Pharaoh') and the series *I racconti della vita* ('Tales of Life'), *Storia di tutti I tempi* ('History of All Times') and *Storie d'oro e di frontiera* ('Stories of Gold and Frontiers'). Using the words of Guiseppe Ramello he produced a series of tales inspired by the Bible and Gospels, and using the words of Tommaso Mastrandrea *Il segreto dei Quattro codici* ('The Secret of the Four Codices') which tells the story of the life of Don Giaccomo Alberione, the founder of the Society of St Paul. Recently, in addition to drawing Karol Wotyla, he has written and designed *Il richiamo della foresta* ('The Call of the Forest') taken from the famous novel by Jack London, and *Le avventure di Robinson Crusoe* ('The Adventures of Robinson Crusoe') taken from Daniel Defoe's book. Using the words of Gino D'Antonio he produced the series of comic adventure books *Magda e Moroni* ('Magda and Moroni'). Author of international fame, Toppi has received many prizes, including the 'Yellow Kid' in 1975.

Translated from the Italian by Andrew Tulloch

ST PAULS
Morpeth Terrace, Victoria, London SW1P 1EP

© *Periodici San Paolo S.r.l. Milan, Italy 2001*
© English translation: ST PAULS, London 2001

ISBN 085439 627 6

Set by TuKan, Fareham, Hampshire, UK
Printed by Stabilimento rotocalcografico Periodici San Paolo
Via Liberazione 4 - 12051 Alba (Cuneo)

ST PAULS is an activity of the priests and brothers
of the Society of St Paul who proclaim the Gospel
through the media of social communication

THE
YEARS
OF HIS YOUTH

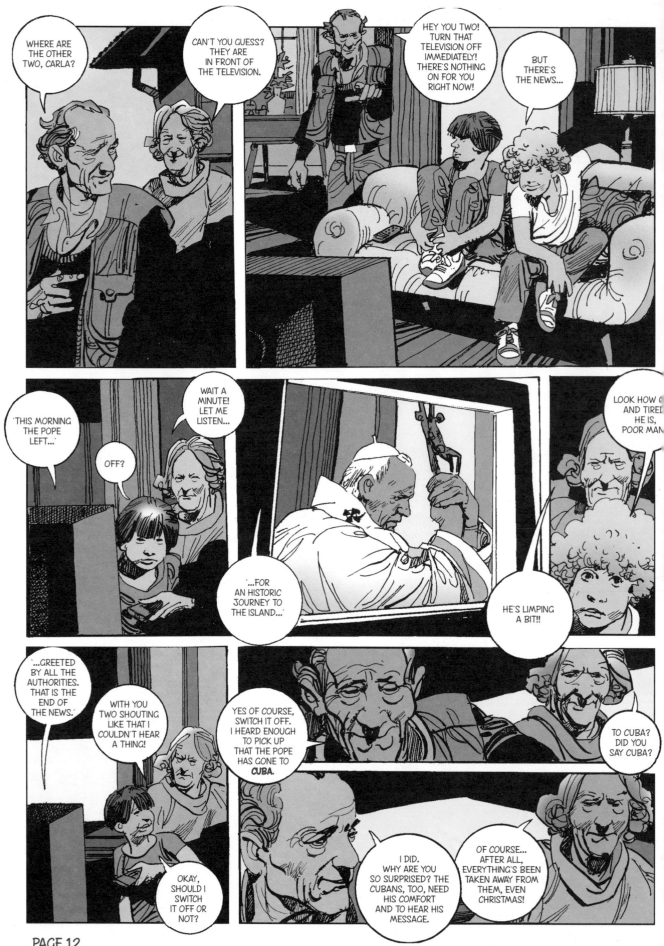

'AND ONE DAY, JUST AFTER HE HAD RETURNED FROM A GAME AT SCHOOL...'

DEAR... YOUR MOTHER HAS GONE TO HEAVEN.

WHAT'S HAPPENED?

KAROL, MY LITTLE ONE, COME WITH ME...

WHAT'S UP, MRS. SOPHIA?

NOOOOOO..!!

NO. I THINK IT MUST HAVE GROWN GRADUALLY. HE CAME FROM A LOVING CHRISTIAN FAMILY, AND WHEN HE WAS YOUNG HE LIVED THROUGH SOME DRAMATIC EVENTS.

THAT WAS IN APRIL 1929 AND KAROL WAS 9 YEARS OLD.

POOR HIM! HOW SAD HE MUST HAVE BEEN...

PERHAPS THAT WAS THE START OF HIS RELIGIOUS VOCATION?

'NONE OF THIS EXPLAINS WHY HIS BROTHER EDMUND, WHO WAS 14 YEARS OLDER, DIDN'T HAVE THE SAME VOCATION AND BECAME A DOCTOR.'

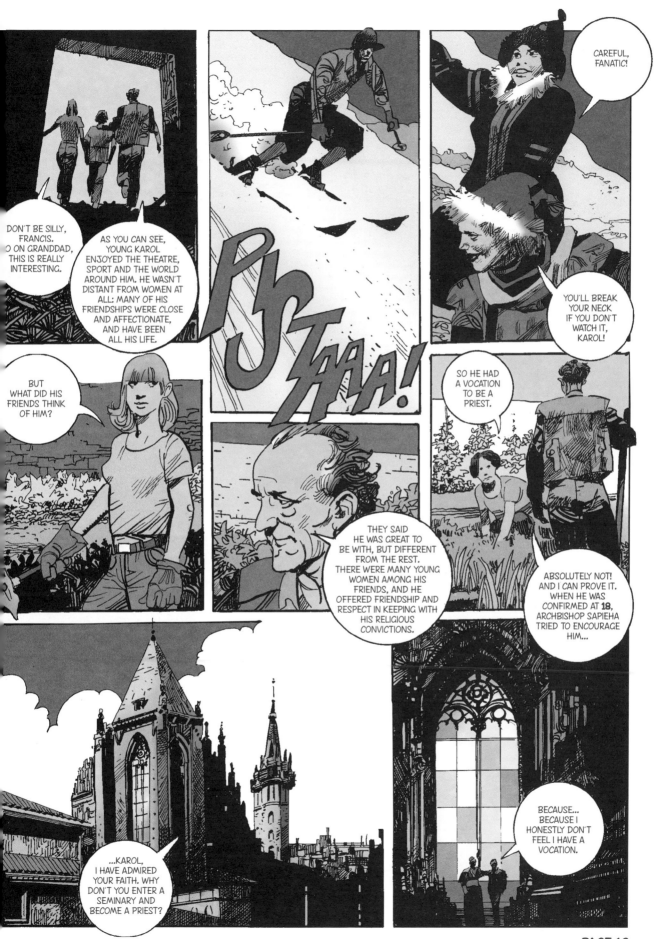

IN
THE STORM
OF WAR

TO THE SEMINARY. YOU MUST LEAVE HERE. THE ARCHBISHOP WILL ORDAIN YOU.

OKAY. I'LL COME IN A MINUTE!... WHAT ABOUT OUR SECRECY?

HURRY UP, BEFORE THE BOMBING STARTS!

RUN! RUN! THERE ISN'T A MOMENT TO LOSE!

STAY WITH US, LORD... DO NOT DESERT US...

'THE POLISH PEOPLE ROSE AGAINST THOSE WHO HAD LONG TRODDEN THEIR HOMELAND UNDERFOOT. AND THE GERMAN RESPONSE WAS VIOLENT.'

'IN THOSE DAYS POLAND LIVED THROUGH SOME TRULY TERRIBLE MOMENTS. UNDER THE BLOWS OF THE SOVIET ARMS THE GERMAN ARMY SLOWLY WITHDREW TO ITS OWN BORDERS, AND POLISH SOIL ONCE MORE BECAME THE FIELD OF BITTER AND BLOODY BATTLES.'

THANK YOU, BROTHERS, THANK YOU. YOU WILL ALWAYS BE IN MY HEART...

IN THE NAME OF THE FATHER, AND OF THE SON AND OF THE HOLY SPIRIT!

A FEW DAYS LATER THE YOUNG PRIEST BAPTIZED THE DAUGHTER OF TWO OLD FRIENDS FROM THE AMATEUR THEATRE COMPANY...

THAT MAYBE SO, KAROL. BUT MAYBE IT WAS WRITTEN THAT ONE DAY YOU WOULD BAPTIZE OUR DAUGHTER?

THE GREAT DIRECTOR ABOVE ARRANGES EVERYTHING FOR OUR GOOD, BELIEVE ME.

HALINA! TADEUS! IT WASN'T IN THE SCRIPT THAT YOU SHOULD CRY IN THIS SCENE!

BY BAPTIZING HIS FRIENDS' DAUGHTER KAROL SHOWED HE STILL HAD A DEEP AFFECTION FOR THE WORLD OF THE THEATRE. HIS VOCATION HAD GROWN IN THAT WORLD AND HE REMAINED INVOLVED IN IT FOR AS LONG AS HE STAYED IN HIS HOMELAND.

WHAT WAS HIS FIRST JOB AS A PRIEST?

FIRST JOB? TO PACK HIS BAGS AND HEAD FOR ROME TO STUDY MORE THEOLOGY AT THE 'ANGELICUM' WITH THE DOMINICAN FATHERS. IT WAS **1946**.

FINALLY A BREAK A SOME RES

FROM CRACOW
TO ROME

KAROL CERTAINLY WASN'T THE TYPE TO GET EASILY FRIGHTENED. HE HAD FAITH. HE AVOIDED GETTING MIXED UP IN POLITICS AND CONCENTRATED ON TRYING TO BECOME A BETTER PRIEST...

...BUT HE COULD NOT ACCEPT THAT HIS PEOPLE WERE NOT FREE TO PRAY AND THAT THE PERSON SHOULD BE OWNED BY THE STATE, WHICH WAS WHAT THE SOVIETS WANTED!

IN FACT THE **STUBBORN** RESISTANCE OF POLISH CATHOLICS PROVOKED THE REGIME INTO OPEN HOSTILITY AGAINST THE CHURCH.

WHAT'S HAPPENED? WHY HAVEN'T YOU GONE IN?

RUSSIAN SOLDIERS HAVE BLOCKED OFF THE ENTRANCE.

LOOK, PROFESSOR!

`THIS HAPPENED IN **1953**, WHEN KAROL WAS TEACHING MORAL THEOLOGY AT THE JAGIELLONIAN UNIVERSITY IN CRACOW.´

GRANDDAD, THAT'S EXACTLY WHAT ANOTHER REGIME DID, ISN'T IT?

YES. ABSOLUTELY BARBAROUS!

KAROL GOT ANOTHER TEACHING POST AT LUBLIN AND THREW HIMSELF WITH GREAT ARDOUR INTO HIS MISSION AS A PRIEST AND TEACHER. **5** YEARS OF INTENSE ACTIVITY FOLLOWED.

PAGE 39

HIS OLD PASSION FOR THE THEATRE AND POETRY, WHICH HE HAD NEVER LOST, RESURFACED.

DID HE WRITE ANY PLAYS?

OF COURSE! ONE WAS CALLED 'THE JEWELLER'S SHOP'...

HE WROTE IT? I REMEMBER HEARING IT WAS PERFORMED HERE IN ITALY, AND WAS QUITE SUCCESSFUL...

NEVERTHELESS, POLISH CATHOLICS KNEW HIM AS A PRIEST AND SCHOLAR, NOT AS A WRITER. HUMAN RIGHTS, THE RIGHTS OF THE FAMILY AND THE DEFENCE OF LIFE ARE THE CONSTANT SUBJECTS OF HIS TEACHING AND PREACHING IN THE LIGHT OF THE GOSPEL.

`AND SO, ON **4TH JULY 1958** POPE PIUS XII DECIDED TO APPOINT HIM AUXILIARY BISHOP OF CRACOW. KAROL WAS ONLY **38**, AND THE YOUNGEST POLISH BISHOP.´

BRAVO! THAT QUARRYMAN DESERVED IT!

WRRRRRRRRRR

IN 1962 HE WAS NOMINATED VICAR-CAPITULAR... AND FROM 1962 TO 1965 HE TOOK AN ACTIVE PART IN THE SECOND VATICAN COUNCIL. HE STOOD OUT AS A WITNESS OF A MARGINALIZED AND SUFFERING CHURCH, A CHURCH THAT WAS THE ONLY BULWARK OF FREEDOM BEHIND THE 'IRON CURTAIN'.*

*IRON CURTAIN: A LINE THROUGH EUROPE WHICH DIVIDED THE STATES UNDER COMMUNIST RULE AND THOSE WHICH WERE FREE AND DEMOCRATIC.

PHEW! WHAT A CAREER! HOW BUSY HE WAS!

HE WAS NOT ONLY BUSY DOING THINGS, BUT PRAYING AS WELL.

AT THAT TIME SOMETHING HAPPENED THAT WAS CLOSELY CONNECTED WITH PRAYER...

'BISHOP WOJTYLA WAS LOOKING SAD AND WORRIED BECAUSE OF SOME NEWS HE'D RECEIVED FROM HOME.'

EXCELLENCY, I CAN SEE YOU ARE PREOCCUPIED. HAVE YOU RECEIVED SOME BAD NEWS?

UNFORTUNATELY YES. A FRIEND FROM THE UNIVERSITY, WANDA POLTAWASKA, A PSYCHIATRIST AND MOTHER OF FOUR, HAS A MALIGN TUMOUR IN HER THROAT AND SHE IS DYING.

I'M SO SORRY...I WISH I COULD DO SOMETHING.

ALL WE CAN DO IS PRAY.

WHILE HE WAS PRAYING KAROL'S EYE STRAYED ONTO A BIOGRAPHY OF PADRE PIO. KAROL HAD MET HIM IN 1946, WHEN HE WAS STUDYING THEOLOGY AT ROME.

'IMMEDIATELY HE TOOK A PEN AND SOME PAPER...'

'VENERABLE FATHER, I ASK YOU TO PRAY FOR A MOTHER OF FOUR CHILDREN WHO IS 40 YEARS OLD AND LIVES IN CRACOW.'

'DURING THE LAST WAR SHE WAS A PRISONER IN CONCENTRATION CAMP IN GERMANY, AND NOW HER LIFE IS THREATENED BY CANCER.'

'PRAY THAT GOD, THROUGH THE INTERCESSION OF THE BLESSED VIRGIN MARY, WILL SHOW MERCY TO HER AND HER FAMILY. I AM DEEPLY INDEBTED TO YOU. YOURS IN CHRIST. KAROL WOJTYLA.'

ELEVEN DAYS LATER PADRE PIO RECEIVED ANOTHER MESSAGE...

'DEAR FATHER, I GIVE THANKS TO GOD – AND TO YOU VENERABLE FATHER. I MUST CONVEY THE GREATEST THANKS POSSIBLE ON BEHALF OF THE SAME WOMAN, HER HUSBAND AND THE ENTIRE FAMILY.'

WHAT HAPPENED?

A MIRACLE, MY DEAR. THE TUMOUR DISAPPEARED AND THE LADY IS STILL ALIVE TODAY, ENJOYING FULL HEALTH.

SURPRISED, ARE YOU? RIGHT, LET'S CONTINUE OUR LITTLE STORY.

WHILE THE SECOND VATICAN COUNCIL WAS IN FULL SWING, ON **18TH JANUARY 1964**, POPE PAUL VI APPOINTED HIM METROPOLITAN ARCHBISHOP OF CRACOW. HE WAS ONLY **44**!

WHEN HE PUT ON THE OLD VESTMENTS BELONGING TO HIS MEDIEVAL PREDECESSORS, KAROL SAID...

...AND REMEMBER, BROTHERS AND SISTERS, WITHOUT THE CATHOLIC CHURCH POLAND WOULD NEVER HAVE EXISTED!

THE YOUNG ARCHBISHOP HELD THE CROSS HIGH OVER THE HOMELAND HE LOVED. BY THIS ACT HE GAVE STRENGTH AND HOPE TO HIS FELLOW POLES AND TO ALL THOSE OPPRESSED BY THE SOVIET REGIME. THE CHURCH HONOURED HIS DEDICATION, AND SO ON **26TH JUNE 1967** WHILE HE WAS BOATING ON LAKE MAZURI HE HEARD SOMEONE SHOUTING FROM THE SHORE...

YOU'VE DONE ENOUGH ROWING, TADEUS. IT'S MY TURN NOW!

EXCELLENCY! EXCELLENCY!

LET'S GO IN A BIT CLOSER, TADEUS. I THINK SOMETHING'S HAPPENED...

NOW THAT HE'S GONE WE'LL GET IT FROM THE LIEUTENANT. YOU AND YOUR 'NOSE' FOR DISHONESTY!

THIS IS CRAZY: A CARDINAL WHO SKIS!

BUT NEXT TIME I'LL BE MORE CAREFUL! FORGIVE ME FOR DISTURBING YOU. GOODBYE!

'IN 1976 KAROL CELEBRATED THE FIRST THOUSAND YEARS OF CHRISTIANITY IN POLAND WITH THE CARDINAL PRIMATE STEFAN WYSZYNSKI AND THE OTHER POLISH BISHOPS. IT WAS A MOMENT OF GREAT SIGNIFICANCE AT THAT PARTICULAR TIME IN POLITICS.'

WHO COULD EVER HAVE IMAGINED WHEN THEY WERE BEING BAPTIZED ALL THAT TIME AGO THAT SOMEONE FROM THEIR OWN COUNTRY WOULD ONE DAY BECOME THE HEAD OF THE WORLD-WIDE CATHOLIC COMMUNITY!

A PROPHET? SOMEONE WHO COULD FORETELL THE FUTURE?

BUT SOMEONE DID IMAGINE IT LATER ON...

HE WAS A POET CALLED JULIUS SLOWACKI. IN **1848** HE WROTE: 'THE PAPAL THRONE RECEIVES A SLAVIC POPE... HE COURAGEOUSLY CONFRONTS THE SWORD; THE WORLD IS BUT DUST TO HIM... SEE, THE SLAVIC POPE MOVES FORWARD, BROTHER OF THE PEOPLE!'

'WHEN HE BECAME POPE, JOHN PAUL II LOOKED OUT ONTO A WORLD SHAKEN BY MANY TROUBLES: WAR, HUNGER, UNDERDEVELOPMENT, OPPOSING IDEOLOGIES THAT CAUSED DIVISIONS AND HUMAN VICTIMS: THE THIRD WORLD WITH ITS UNRESOLVED PROBLEMS AND IN EUROPE THERE WAS THE EYESORE OF THE BERLIN WALL...'

PILGRIM
OF PEACE
THROUGH THE
WHOLE WORLD

HE'S A VERY SPECIAL POPE!

YOU'RE RIGHT, CLARA. KAROL WOJTYLA ALWAYS SHOWED WHAT AN EXCEPTIONAL MAN HE WAS, DIDN'T HE, GRAN?

HE CERTAINLY DID... SOON AS HE HAD BEEN MADE POPE HE BROKE THE OLD TRADITION THAT BADE NEWLY-ELECTED POPES TO LEAVE THE VATICAN BEFORE THEY HAD BEEN FORMALLY ENTHRONED.

CAN YOU TELL US A STORY ABOUT HIM...

I CAN. LISTEN...

MONSIGNOR CAPRIO, WOULD YOU BE SO KIND AS TO COME WITH ME TO THE GEMELLI GENERAL HOSPITAL?

EHM... OF COURSE, YOUR HOLINESS. MIGHT I ASK WHY?

I WANT TO GO AND SEE MY DEAR FRIEND BISHOP DESKUR.

AFTER ARRIVING AT THE HOSPITAL AND SEEING HIS FRIEND, HE WENT TO VISIT THE OTHER WARDS, TALKING QUIETLY WITH THE MEDICAL STAFF AND PATIENTS.

JUST AS HE WAS ABOUT TO LEAVE...

HOLINESS, HOLINESS... YOU MUST GIVE A BLESSING...

AH YES, DEAR BROTHERS AND SISTERS! THE VISIT ISN'T FINIS YET. MONSIGNOR CA IS TEACHING ME H A POPE SHOUL BEHAVE: I HAVE ST TO GIVE MY BLESSING...

IN NOMINE PATRIS ET FILII ET...

THAT'S PRETTY AMAZING!

YOU MUST ADMIT THAT ON THAT OCCASION HE SHOWED THAT HE HAD THE GREATNESS OF A LEADER AND THE HUMILITY OF A NEWCOMER.

HUMILITY... THE GREAT VIRTUE THAT THIS AGE HAS FORGOTTEN. ALL THAT SEEMS TO COUNT TODAY IS THE RIGHT IMAGE, AND PRIDE.

GRAN! WE'VE FINISHED OUR SNACK. CAN WE WATCH TELEVISION?

THERE MIGHT BE A GOOD PROGRAMME ON.

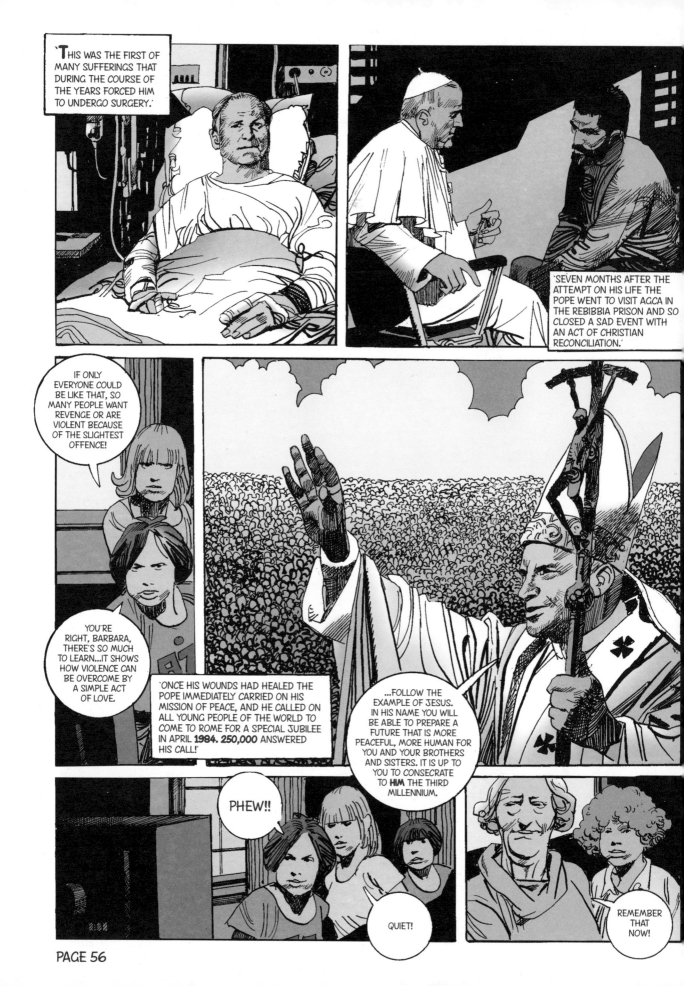

VERY GOOD! IT'S A SHAME THAT SOME THINK DIFFERENTLY... FANATICISM IS AN EXTREMELY UGLY THING IN ANY AREA OF LIFE.

EVEN ON THE FOOTBALL PITCH! JUST THINK OF ALL THE PUNCHING THAT GOES ON EVERY SUNDAY.

BUT WHAT'S THAT GOT TO DO WITH WHAT THE POPE SAID? YOU HAVEN'T UNDERSTOOD A THING...

NOT UNDERSTOOD A THING? WHENEVER W GLORIFY A DOCTRINE W BELIEVE IN, OR A POLITIC PARTY OR THE COLOURS A TEAM, WE EASILY FAL INTO A FANATICAL PASSIO AND PRODUCE RESULTS WHICH ARE TRAGICALLY SIMILAR.

YOU'RE RIGHT, GRANDDAD. THAT KIND OF ATTITUDE ISN'T VERY CHRISTIAN.

THIS MESSAGE OF PEACE AND UNDERSTANDING OVERCOMES ANY SORT OF BARRIER, HISTORICAL OR OTHERWISE. SPOKEN IN A HUMBLE SINCERITY TYPICAL OF CATHOLICISM, IT SOON BEGAN TO BRING FORTH GOOD FRUITS.

AT ASSISI, ON **27TH OCTOBER 1986**, FOR THE FIRST TIME IN THE HISTORY OF THE WORLD, REPRESENTATIVES OF ALL RELIGIONS CAME TOGETHER AND PRAYED TOGETHER FOR PEACE.

THE FACT THAT WE ARE GATHERED HERE TODAY DOES NOT IMPLY THAT WE HAVE ANY INTENTION TO SEARCH FOR RELIGIOUS AGREEMENT AMONG US, OR TO SELL OUR OWN CONVICTIONS SHORT...

...IT DOES MEAN THAT ALL RELIGIONS CAN COME TOGETHER AND WORK ON A COMMON TASK, ON AN EARTHLY PROJECT WHICH IN A SENSE GOES BEYOND THEM. SO WE WILL NOT WASTE TIME ARGUING ABOUT WHO IS RIGHT. EVERY PERSON MUST BE ALLOWED TO FOLLOW THEIR JUST CONSCIENCE AS THEY STRIVE TO OBEY THE TRUTH.

'NOT ONE OF THE RELIGIOUS LEADERS GATHERED IN THE CITY OF ST FRANCIS DISAGREED WITH THIS MESSAGE OF PEACE, GIVEN BY THE CATHOLIC CHURCH THROUGH THE POPE.'

BUT THE POPE HAD CHOSEN TO PREACH TO A MUCH WIDER AUDIENCE THAN THOSE GATHERED IN THE BASILICA AT ASSISI OR ST PETER'S SQUARE: **THE ENTIRE PLANET!**

I WANT TO GO TO ALL THOSE WHO PRAY, FROM THE BEDOUIN IN THE DESERT TO THE SISTER IN HER CONVENT...

...TO THOSE WHO ARE ACTIVE AND AT THE VERY HEIGHT OF THEIR POWERS...

...TO THE SICK ON THEIR BED OF SUFFERING...

IT WAS NOT ANY ARMY WITH ITS NUCLEAR THREAT WHICH BROUGHT THE IRON CURTAIN DOWN, IT WAS NOT THE STRATEGY OF STAR WARS...

...BUT THE WORK OF UNARMED AND COURAGEOUS MEN. IT WAS NOT **NATO** WITH ITS MISSILES, BUT A FEARLESS CATHOLIC UNION THAT CARRIED IMAGES OF THE MADONNA AND USED THE ROSARY AS ITS WEAPON!

AND SO THE FAITH OF A POPE 'FROM A FARAWAY COUNTRY' SWEPT AWAY THE SOVIET EMPIRE AND, WITHOUT VIOLENCE, REMOVED THE HORRORS OF BLOOD THAT HAD BEEN SO ABUNDANTLY SHED.

A MIRACLE! DID YOU SEE HOW SOMETHING THAT FOR YEARS WAS CONSIDERED ONLY A DREAM BECAME REALITY IN A SINGLE MOMENT?

'THIS WAVE OF FREEDOM SWEPT ALL BEFORE IT AND LED TO AN EVENT THAT WOULD HAVE BEEN UNTHINKABLE A FEW YEARS EARLIER. **MIKHAIL GORBACHEV**, PRESIDENT OF THE CRUMBLING SOVIET EMPIRE WENT TO SEE THE POPE AND THE WORLD WAS AT FIRST ASTONISHED AND THEN MOVED.'

"AND SO THIS DIFFERENT POPE WAS THE FIRST POPE SINCE THE TIME OF THE FRENCH REVOLUTION TO LIVE THE WORLD-WIDE MISSION OF THE CATHOLIC CHURCH, CAPABLE OF CHANGING THE FACE OF THE EARTH."

...ALL YOU WHO HAVE ALREADY THE GREAT GOOD FORTUNE TO BELIEVE, ALL YOU WHO ARE SEARCHING FOR GOD, AND EVEN YOU WHO ARE TORMENTED BY DOUBTS, I TELL YOU, DO NOT BE AFRAID TO ACCEPT CHRIST AND HIS POWER! IT IS NOT THAT AN OLD WORLD IS DYING, BUT THAT A NEW ONE IS BEING BORN!

MY DEAR GRANDCHILDREN!... THEY'VE UNDERSTOOD...

THIS POPE, FORMED IN SOLITUDE AND SUFFERING, HAS FACED THE WORLD LIKE A COMMANDER AND COME OUT COVERED WITH WOUNDS. SUFFERING HAS WORN DOWN HIS CHAMPION'S CONSTITUTION...

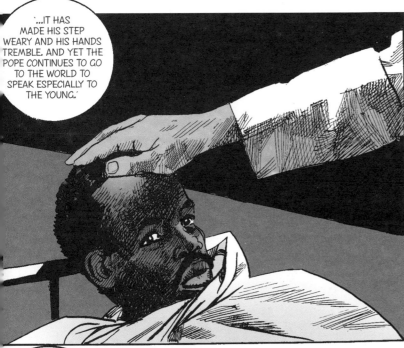

'...IT HAS MADE HIS STEP WEARY AND HIS HANDS TREMBLE. AND YET THE POPE CONTINUES TO GO TO THE WORLD TO SPEAK ESPECIALLY TO THE YOUNG.'

WHICH COUNTRY IS THAT?

SSSH! LET ME LISTEN.

YOUR TASK IS AN IMMENSE ONE, TO OVERCOME ALL EVIL WITH GOOD, TRYING ALWAYS IN THE MIDST OF LIFE'S DIFFICULTIES TO PLACE YOUR TRUST IN GOD.

RATHER THAN ONLY IN THE WORDS OF THE MANY SELF-INTERESTED 'MESSIAHS' OF TODAY WHO JUST APPEAR FROM NOWHERE...

AND YOU YOUNG PEOPLE MUST OPPOSE ANY FORM OF HATRED WITH THE INVINCIBLE POWER OF CHRIST'S LOVE...

...THIS MEANS – YOU MUST BE WORKERS FOR PEACE AND MUST BUILD THE PEACE OF CHRIST'S KINGDOM!

NEVER FORGET THAT! IT'S UP TO YOU TO BUILD A BETTER WORLD AND A BETTER FUTURE.

THE YOUNG PEOPLE! HIS GREAT HOPE! AT HIS EVERY INVITATION THOUSANDS CAME TO MEET HIM: AT BUENOS AIRES, SANTIAGO DE COMPOSTELLA, CZESTOCHOWA, DENVER, MANILA, PARIS AND ROME!

PAGE 63

Important Moments in the Life of Karol Wojtyla

18 May 1920
Karol Józef Wojtyla, son of Karol and Emilia Kaczorowska. Born on 18 March 1920, in Wadowice (Cracow), baptised by the military chaplain, Fr Franciszek Zak on 20 June 1920. He lives with his parents at 2, Rynek (today Flat 4, 7 Koscielna Street).

13 April 1929
Death of his mother, Emilia Kaczorowska.

June 1930
Karol enters Marcin Wadowita Grammar School.

5 December 1932
EdmundWojtila, Karol's older brother, dies.

1934-1938
First appearances in the students' theatre at Wadowice. During his time at the grammar school he is president of the Marian sodality. During these years he also goes on his first pilgrimage to Czestochowa.

September 1935
Takes part in exercises at the Military Training Division at Hermanice.

22 June 1938
Applies for a place in the faculty of philosophy (studying Polish philology) at the Jagiellonian University in Cracow. Beginning of the academic year Karol takes up residence at Cracow. While studying at university, he joins Studio 38, a drama circle founded by Tadeusz Kudlinski.

July 1939
Social training camps of the University Legion at Ozomla, near Sadowa Wiszna, for Polish and Ukrainian students.

1 September 1939
Second World War begins.

18 February 1941
His father dies after a heart attack: Karol is on his own. In March, he commences work as a labourer in the quarry at Zakrzówek, with his friend Kotlarezyk he founds the Rhapsodic Theatre of Cracow.

1 November 1941
First staging of Król Duch ('Royal Spirit'), by Juliusz Slowacki.

Spring 1942
Transferred from the quarry to the Solvay factory.

October 1942
Begins to attend underground courses held by the Jagiellonian University's Faculty of Theology as a seminarian of the Archdiocese of Cracow.

March 1943
First staging of Samuel Zborowski by Juliusz Slowacki. Karol Wojtyla takes the leading role. His last appearance on stage.

1 November 1946
He is ordained a priest and receives holy orders from the hands of the Metropolitan Archbishop Adam Sapieha.

26 November 1946
Arrives at Rome for further study and enrols at the Angelicum.

14 June 1948
Completes his studies with a dissertation on 'The Doctrine of Faith according to St John of the Cross'. He then returns to Poland and is sent as a curate first to a parish at Niegowic and then to another in Cracow.

From October 1953
Teaches Catholic social ethics at the Theology Faculty of the Jagiellonian University.

From 1 December 1956
Lectures in Ethics at the Catholic University of Lublin. He keeps this position until 16 October 1978.

4 July 1958
Appointed auxiliary bishop to the Archbishop of Cracow, Monsignor Eugeniusz Baziak.

5 October 1962
Leaves to take part in the Second Vatican Council, in the sessions held between 11 October and 8 December.

5-15 December 1963
Pilgrimage to the Holy Land in the company of bishops from different nations attending the Council.

30 December 1963
Appointed Metropolitan Archbishop of Cracow.

28 June 1967
Created cardinal by Pope Paul VI.

2-9 March 1973
Takes part in the Eucharistic Congress of Australia. Stops over at Manila and New Guinea.

7-13 March 1976
Preaches the Lenten Exercises in the Vatican.

23 June 1977
Made honorary doctor by Johannes Gutenberg University in Mainz.

21 June 1978
Gives a talk on 'Marriage and Love' at the CISF Congress, held on the tenth anniversary of the Encyclical letter Humanae Vitae, in the main offices of Saint Pauls Periodicals, the publishers of Famiglia Cristiana ('Christian Family') and Il Giornalino.

16 October 1978 (approx. 5.15 pm)
Cardinal Karol Wojtyla is elected Pope and takes the name of John Paul II. He is the 263rd successor of Peter.

10 November 1979
Announces that the case of Galileo will be 're-examined'.

Left:
Karol Wojtyla aged 18, and a member of the drama circle Studio 18.

Right:
Cardinal Wojtyla gives a talk on 'Marriage and Love' at the CISF Congress.

Top & Right: *John Paul II among the youth, celebrating XV World Youth Day, 19 August 2000, on the Campus of the University of Tor Vergata, Rome.*

Right: *6 January 2001, end of the Great Jubilee. John Paul II closes the 'Holy Door' of St Peter's Basilica, Vatican City.*

26 September 1980
Convokes the Bishops' Synod on 'The Task of the Christian Family in the World of Today'.

13 May 1981
An attempt is made on his life in St Peter's Square.

26 January 1983
Promulgates the new Code of Canon Law.

25 March 1983
Opens the Holy Year of the Redemption.

29 September 1983
Convokes the Bishops' Synod on 'Penance and Reconciliation in the Life of the Church'.

27 December 1983
Meets with his would-be assassin, Alì Agca, in the Rebibbia prison.

31 March 1985
Publishes the Apostolic Letter *To the Young People of the World* on the occasion of the International Year of Youth.

13 April 1986
Visits the Synagogue of Rome.

27 October 1986
Presides over the Assisi Day of Prayer for Peace in the World, in the company of representatives of the world religions.

6 June 1987
Opens the Marian Year in St Peter's Square.

3-7 December 1987
Receives the visit in the Vatican of the Ecumenical Patriarch of Constantinople, Dimitrios I.

12 July 1992
Recovery in the Gemelli Hospital following the removal of a tumour from his colon.

7 December 1992
The new *Catechism of the Catholic Church* is published.

14 November 1994
Publishes the Apostolic Letter *Terzio millennio adveniente* in preparation for the Great Jubilee. In the letter, he proposes to examine the 'dark pages' in the history of the Church at the end of the millennium.

10 July 1995
Publishes a letter to women for the International Year of the Woman.

24 March 1997
Official launch of the Holy See's website on the Internet.

12 April 1997
Pastoral visit to Sarajevo.

16 March 1998
Sends a letter to accompany *We remember: a reflection on the Shoah*, published by the Commission for Religious Relations with the Jews.

28 October 1999
Concludes, in St Peter's Square, the interreligious assembly 'On the Threshold of the Third Millennium: Collaboration between the different religions'.

24 December 1999
The Great Jubilee Year of 2000: opens the Holy Door of Saint Peter's Basilica.

2 January 2000
Jubilee Year of the Children. Presents the sixth international John XXIII Peace Prize to the '*Aide à toute détresse – Quart Monde*' ('Help to all distress – Fourth World').

24 February 2000
Jubilee pilgrimage to Mount Sinai (Egypt).

12 March 2000
Celebration of the Day of Pardon of the Holy Year 2000 at Saint Peter's Basilica. International Theological Commission publishes 'Memory and Reconciliation: the Church and Faults of the Past'.

20 March 2000
Jubilee pilgrimage to the Holy Land (Jordan, Autonomous Territories of the National Palestinian Authorities, Israel and Jerusalem).

12 May 2000
Journeys to Fatima for the beatification – on 13 May – of the shepherd boy Francesco and the shepherd girl Jacinta Marto.

15-20 August 2000
Celebrates the XV World Day of Youth: more than two million young people are present at the Campus of the University of Tor Vergata (Rome) for their jubilee with the Pope.

Journeys of the World's Pilgrim

1979

1   **25 January - 1 February**
Dominican Republic, Mexico, Bahamas

2   **2 - 10 June**
Poland

3   **29 September - 8 October**
Ireland and USA

4   **28 - 30 November**
Turkey

1980

5   **2 - 12 May**
Zaire, Congo, Kenya, Ghana, Upper Volta, Ivory Coast

6   **30 May - 2 June**
France

7   **30 June - 12 July**
Brazil

8   **15 - 19 November**
West Germany

1981

9   **16 - 27 February**
Pakistan, Philippines, USA (Guam and Anchorage), Japan

1982

10   **12 - 19 February**
Nigeria, Benin, Gabon, Equatorial Guinea

11   **12 - 15 May**
Portugal

12   **28 May - 2 June**
Great Britain

13   **10 - 13 June**
Argentina and Brazil (2nd visit)

14   **15 June**
Geneva

15   **29 August**
San Marino

16   **31 October - 9 November**
Spain

1983

17   **2 - 10 March**
Costa Rica, Nicaragua, Panama, El Salvador, Guatemala, Honduras, Belize, Haiti

18   **16 - 25 June**
Poland (2nd visit)

19   **14 - 15 August**
Lourdes (2nd visit to France)

20   **10 - 13 September**
Austria

1984

21   **2 - 12 May**
Fairbanks (USA), South Korea, Papua New Guinea, Solomon Islands, Thailand

22   **12 - 17 June**
Switzerland (2nd visit)

23   **9 - 21 September**
Canada

24   **10 - 13 October**
Spain (2nd visit), Dominican Republic, Puerto Rico

POLAND 1979

MEXICO 1979

PAPUA NEW GUINEA 1984

USA 1987

1985

25 **26 January - 6 February**
Venezuela, Ecuador, Peru, Trinidad and Tobago

26 **11 - 21 May**
Holland, Belgium, Luxemburg

27 **8 - 19 August**
Togo, Ivory Coast (2nd visit), Cameroon, Central African Republic, Zaire (2nd visit), Kenya (2nd visit), Morocco

28 **8 September**
Liechtenstein

1986

29 **31 January - 11 February**
India

30 **1 - 8 July**
Colombia & Santa Lucia

31 **4 - 7 October**
France (3rd visit)

32 **18 November - 1 December**
Bangladesh, Singapore, Fiji Islands, New Zealand, Australia, Seychelles

1987

33 **31 March - 13 April**
Uruguay, Chile, Argentina (2nd visit)

34 **30 April - 4 May**
West Germany (2nd visit)

35 **8 - 14 June**
Poland (3rd visit)

36 **10 - 21 September**
USA (2nd visit), Canada (2nd visit)

1988

37 **7 - 19 May**
Uruguay (2nd visit), Bolivia, Peru (2nd visit), Paraguay

38 **23 June**
Austria (2nd visit)

39 **10 - 19 September**
Zimbabwe, Botswana, Lesotho, Swaziland, Mozambique

40 **8 - 11 October**
France (4th visit)

1989

41 **28 April - 6 May**
Madagascar, La Réunion, Zambia, Malawi

42 **1 - 10 June**
Norway, Iceland, Finland, Denmark, Sweden

43 **19 - 21 August**
Spain (3rd visit)

44 **6 - 16 October**
South Korea (2nd visit), Indonesia, Mauritius

1990

45 **25 January - 1 February**
Capo Verde, Guinea-Bissau, Mali, Burkina Faso (2nd visit), Chad

46 **21 - 22 April**
Czechoslovakia

47 **6 - 14 May**
Mexico (2nd visit)

48 **25 - 27 May**
Malta

49 **1 - 10 September**
Tanzania, Burundi, Rwanda, Ivory Coast (3rd visit)

MADAGASCAR 1989

AUSTRALIA 1986

RWANDA 1990

SANTIAGO DE COMPOSTELA (Spain) 1989

1991

50   **10 - 13 May**
Portugal (3rd visit)

51   **1 - 9 June**
Poland (4th visit)

52   **13 - 20 August**
Poland (5th visit), Hungary

53   **12 - 21 October**
Brazil (3rd visit)

1992

54   **19 - 26 February**
Senegal, Gambia, Guinea

55   **4 - 10 June**
Angola, Sao Tome and Principe

56   **9 - 14 October**
Dominican Republic (3rd visit)

1993

57   **3 - 10 February**
Benin (2nd visit), Uganda, Sudan

58   **25 April**
Albania

59   **12 - 17 June**
Spain (4th visit)

60   **9 - 16 August**
Jamaica. Mexico & USA (3rd visit)

61   **4 - 10 September**
Lithuania, Latvia, Estonia

1994

62   **10 -11 September**
Croatia

1995

63   **11 - 21 January**
Philippines (2nd visit), Papua New
Guinea (2nd visit), Australia (2nd visit),
Sri Lanka

64   **20 - 22 May**
Czech Rep. (2nd visit), Poland (6th visit)

65   **3 - 4 June**
Belgium (2nd visit)

66   **30 June - 3 July**
Slovakia (2nd visit)

67   **14 - 20 September**
Cameroon (2nd visit), South Africa,
Kenya (3rd visit)

68   **4 - 9 October**
USA (4th visit)

1996

69   **5 - 12 February**
Guatemala, Nicaragua, El Salvador,
Venezuela (2nd visit to all)

70   **14 April**
Tunisia

71   **17 - 18 May**
Slovenia

72   **21 - 23 June**
Germany (3rd visit)

73   **6 - 7 September**
Hungary (2nd visit)

74   **19 - 22 September**
France (5th visit)

SENEGAL 1992

ANGOLA 1992

ALBANIA 1993
with Mother Teresa
of Calcutta

LITHUANIA 1993

SLOVENIA 1996

1997

75	**12 - 13 April** Sarajevo
76	**25 - 27 April** Czech Republic (3rd visit)
77	**10 - 11 May** Lebanon
78	**31 May - 10 June** Poland (7th visit)
79	**21 - 24 August** France (6th visit)
80	**2 - 6 October** Brazil (4th visit)

1998

81	**21 - 26 January** Cuba
82	**21 - 23 March** Nigeria
83	**19 - 21 June** Austria
84	**2 - 4 October** Croatia

1999

85	**22 - 28 January** Mexico (4th visit) St Louis (USA, 7th)
86	**7 - 9 May** Rumania
87	**5 - 17 June** Poland (7th visit)
88	**19 September** Slovenia (2nd visit)
89	**5 - 9 October** New Delhi (India, 2nd visit), Georgia

2000

90	**24 - 26 February** Egypt, Sinai
91	**20 - 26 March** Jordan, Israel
92	**12 - 13 May** Fatima, (Portugal 4th visit)

CUBA 1998
with Fidel Castro

THE ENCYCLICALS OF JOHN PAUL II

Redemptor hominis
(15 March 1979)
On 'Christ the Redeemer of humankind'. The Pope's first encyclical. In it he sets out the programme for his pontificate.

Dives in Misericordia
(2 December 1980)
On the Fatherhood of God, 'rich in mercy'.

Laborem exercens
(15 September 1981)
On the human person who 'works', that is to say, on human work.

Slavorum Apostoli
(2 July 1985)
On the Christian East and the heritage of the 'Apostles of the Slavs', Cyril and Methodius.

Dominum et vivificantem
(31 May 1986)
On the Holy Spirit who is 'Lord and giver of life' (this encyclical forms a trilogy on the Trinity with *Redemptor hominis* and *Dives in Misericordia*).

Redemptoris Mater
(25 March 1987)
On the cult of Mary, the cult addressed to the 'Mother of the Redeemer'.

Sollicitudo rei socialis
(19 February 1988)
On the 'social care' of the Church.

Redemptoris Missio
(25 January 1991)
On the Church's missionary activity, which derives from the 'mission of the Redeemer'.

Centesimus annus
(2 May 1991)
On social issues, on the 'hundredth anniversary' of Pope Leo XIII's encyclical *Rerum novarum* (this encyclical forms a trilogy on the Church's social doctrine with *Laborem exercens* and *Sollecitudo rei socialis*).

Veritatis splendor
(5 October 1993)
On the foundations of morality, which must be guided by the 'splendour of the truth'.

Evangelium vitae
(31 March 1995)
On abortion, euthanasia and the death penalty, asking humanity at the end of the millennium to take a stand against the culture of death with the 'Gospel of life'.

Ut unum sint
(31 May 1995)
On ecumenism, responding to the prayer of Christ 'that they may be one'. It invites sister Churches to 'seek together' for new ways in which the papacy can be exercised, in ways that are acceptable to all.

Fides et Ratio
(15 October 1998)
On the relation between 'faith and reason' in contemporary thought.